THE THOUGHTS OF WICKED WILLIE

She who sunbathes topless must take the consequences.
She who sunbathes bottomless must take judo lessons.

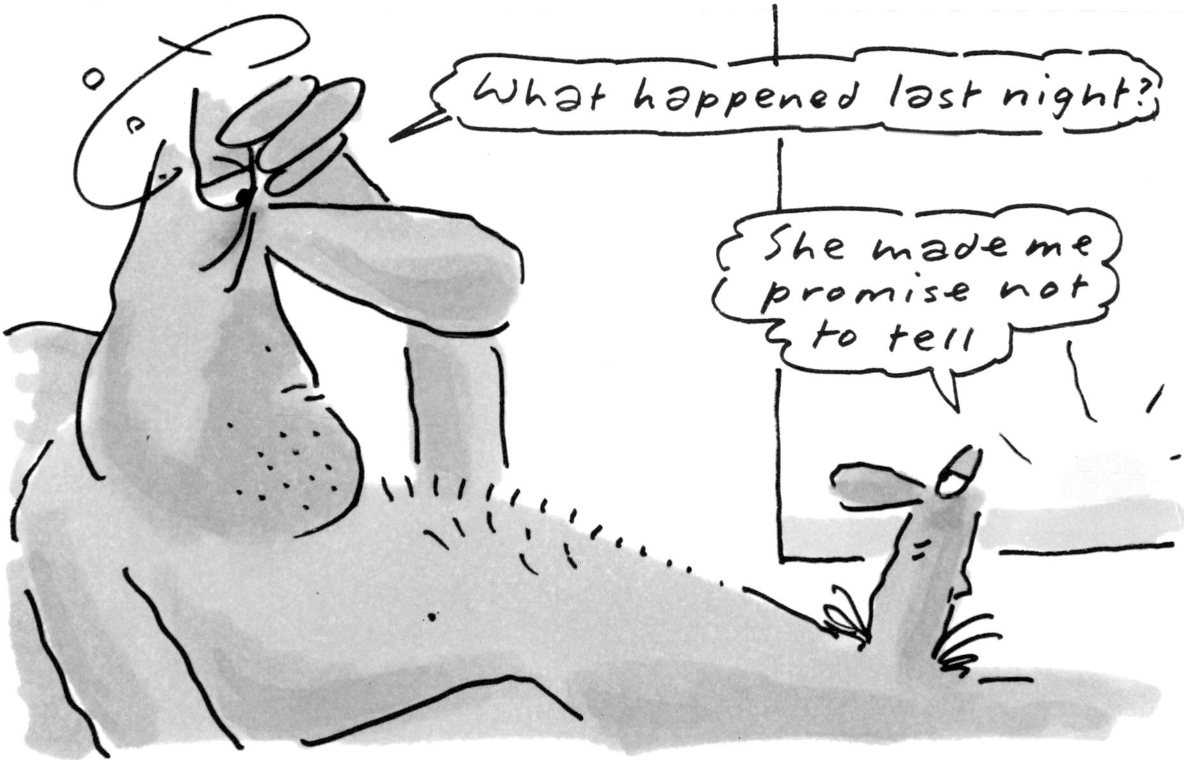
What happened last night?
She made me promise not to tell

THE THOUGHTS OF WICKED WILLIE

Forgetting a face is all very well as long as you remember what you did with the rest of it.

THE THOUGHTS OF WICKED WILLIE
He who can't hold his liquor goes to bed empty-handed.

THE THOUGHTS OF WICKED WILLIE
Swimsuits get smaller as you get older.

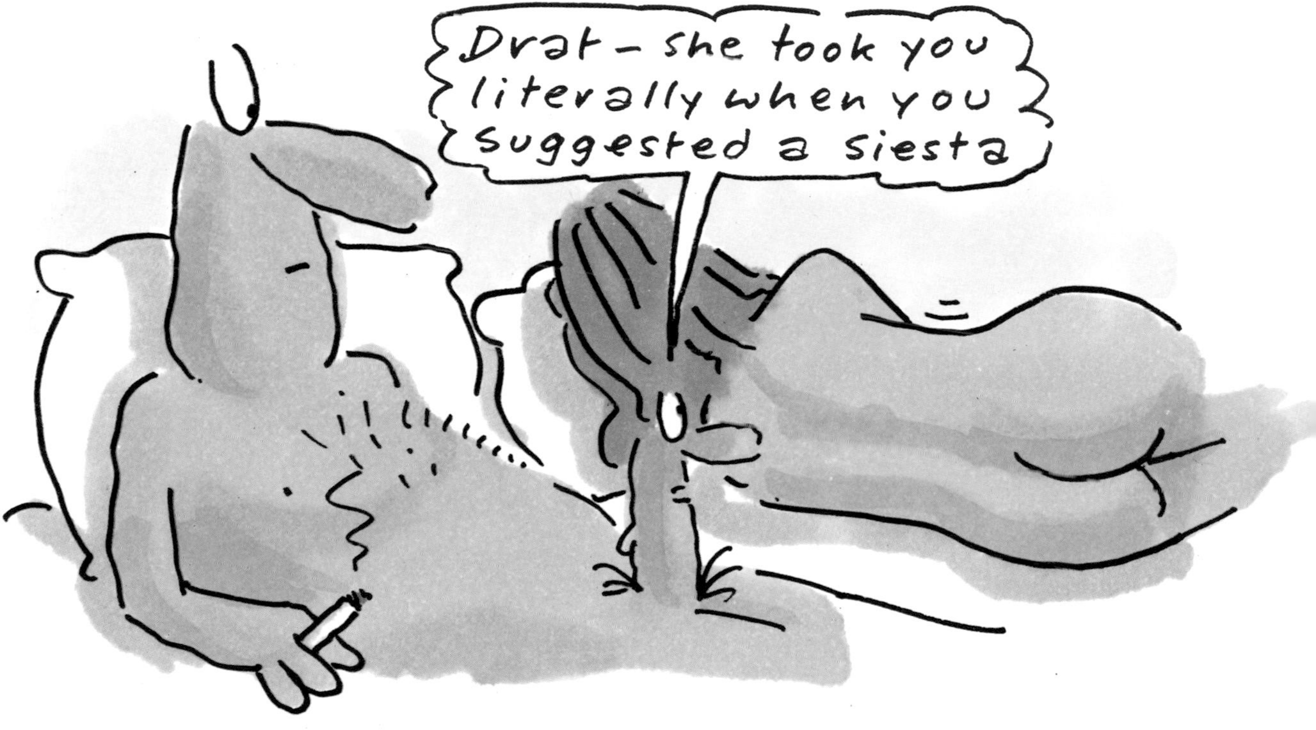
Drat – she took you literally when you suggested a siesta

THE THOUGHTS OF WICKED WILLIE
Headaches can happen after lunch as well as after dinner.

THE THOUGHTS OF WICKED WILLIE
A bird in the sand is worth two in the disco.

THE THOUGHTS OF WICKED WILLIE
Never sunbathe naked. Look what it does to your nose.

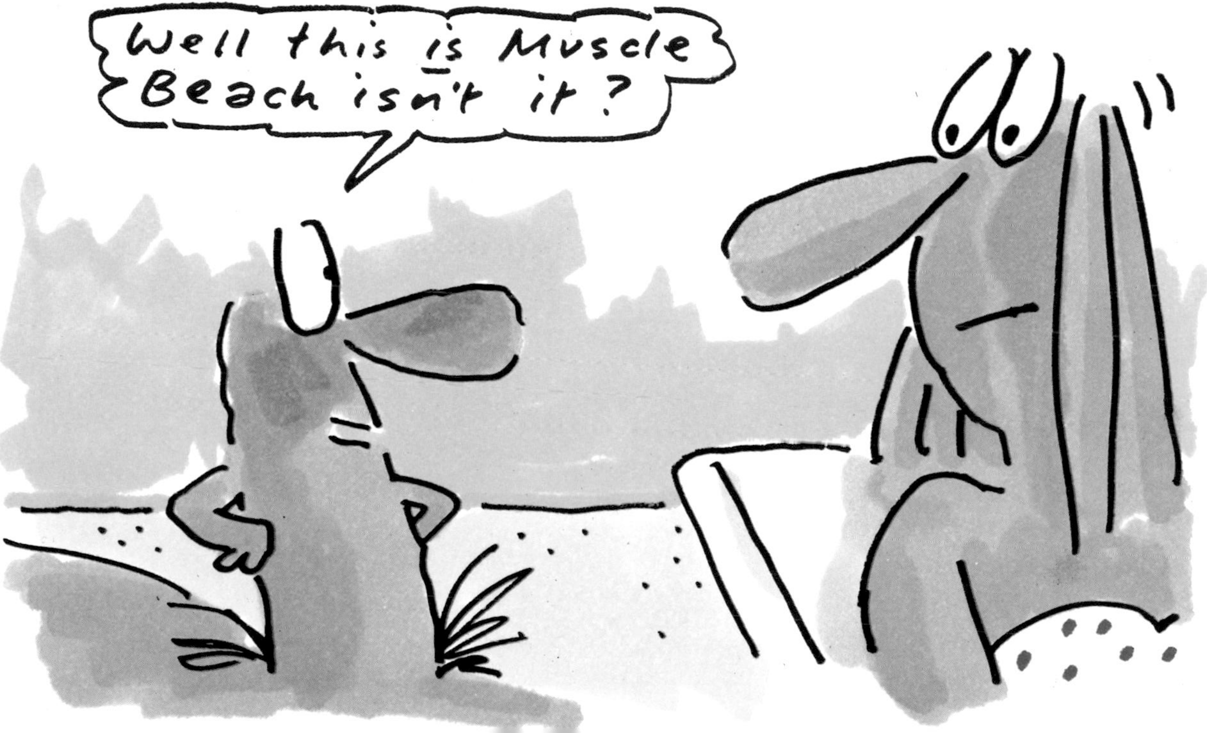
Well this is Muscle Beach isn't it?

THE THOUGHTS OF WICKED WILLIE
You don't need biceps to do push-ups.

THE THOUGHTS OF WICKED WILLIE
Who needs beach balls?

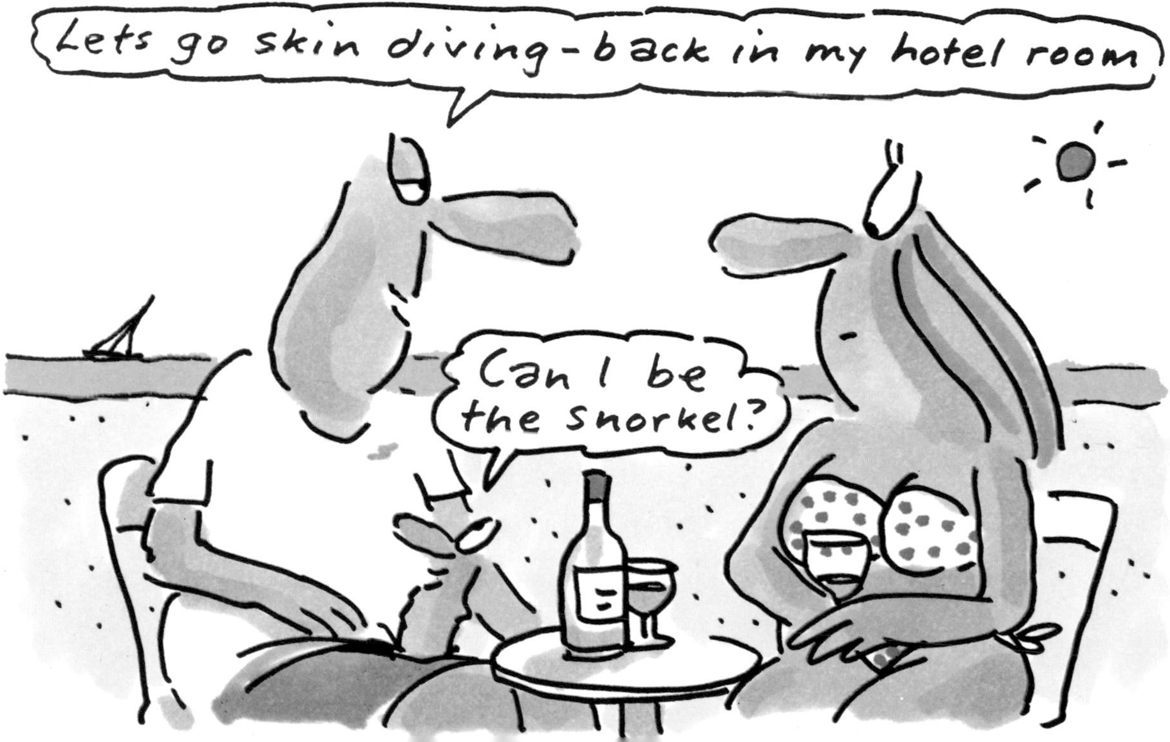
Lets go skin diving-back in my hotel room
Can I be the snorkel?

THE THOUGHTS OF WICKED WILLIE

It is not unflattering to be mistaken for a snorkel as long as you're not expected to blow bubbles.

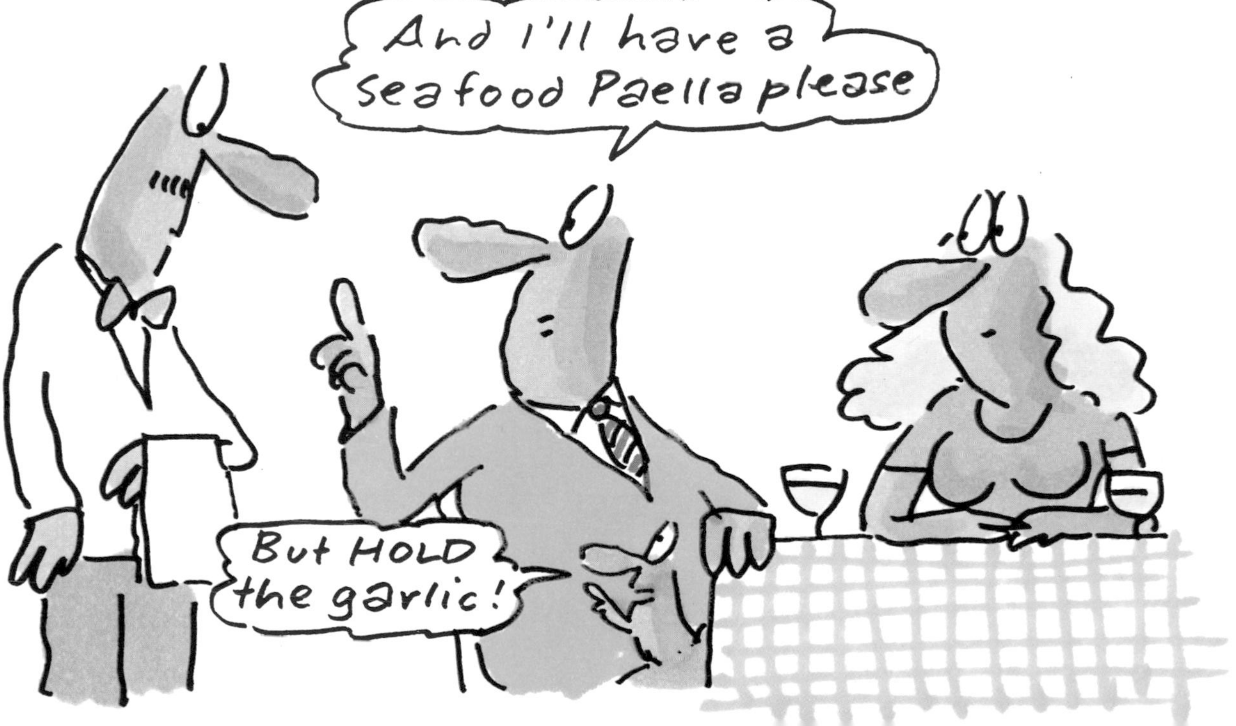
And I'll have a seafood Paella please
But HOLD the garlic!

THE THOUGHTS OF WICKED WILLIE
Local cooking is dangerous. Ask any mussel.

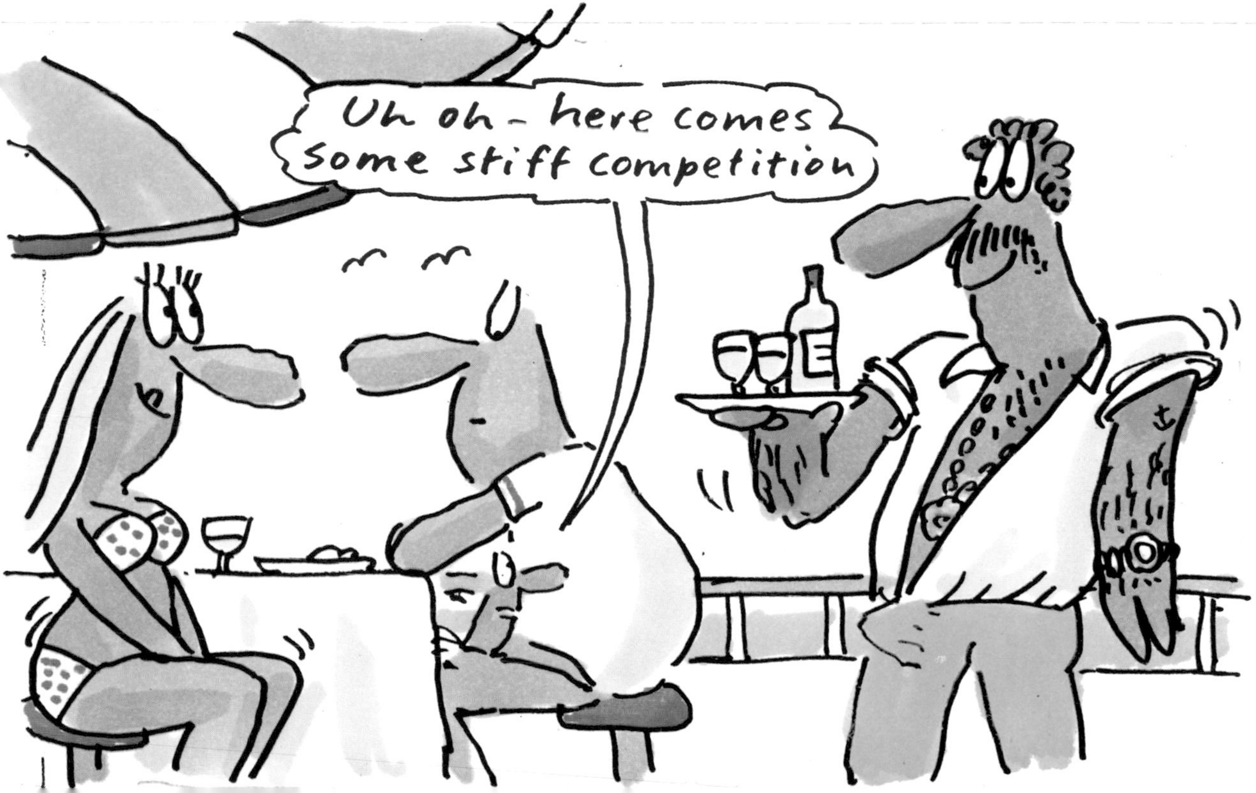
Uh oh - here comes some stiff competition

THE THOUGHTS OF WICKED WILLIE

Beware the waiter who has more than three shirt buttons undone.

THE THOUGHTS OF WICKED WILLIE
Why am I never in holiday snapshots?

I could have sworn 'baiser' meant 'to kiss'..
Not these days, Guv
FRENCH ENGLISH

THE THOUGHTS OF WICKED WILLIE
The man who keeps his mouth shut will never get his face slapped.

Well you may be here for a rest but I'm here for a HOLIDAY!
CLUBS
WAR & PEACE

THE THOUGHTS OF WICKED WILLIE
It's no fun being used as a bookmark.